Page 2

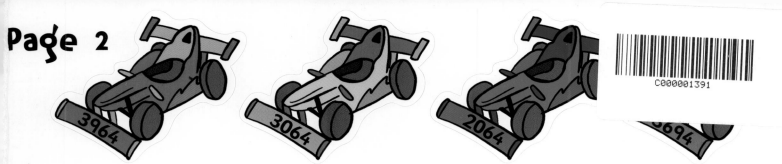

Pages 3, 10, 17, 20 & 28

Page 7

V X X X X X X X X X X X L L L
L L C C C C C C C C C C C C D

Page 13

Page 21

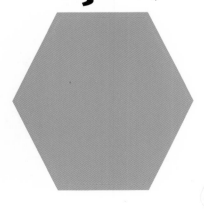

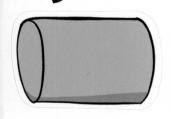 

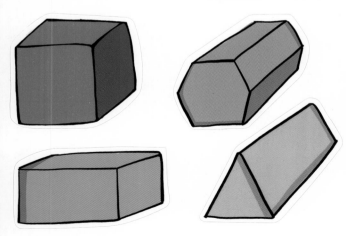

Page 26

regular	regular	regular	regular
irregular	irregular	irregular	irregular

Page 29

Page 36

Page 25

Page 30

Pages 36 & 37

1	3	3	6	6	7	7
8	12	12	13	13	17	18
20	21	23	23	25	37	

Page 42

Moon A
24.5 km
circumference

Moon B
57.1 km
circumference

Moon C
21.09 km
circumference

Moon D
21.9 km
circumference

Moon E
57.7 km
circumference

Reward Stickers

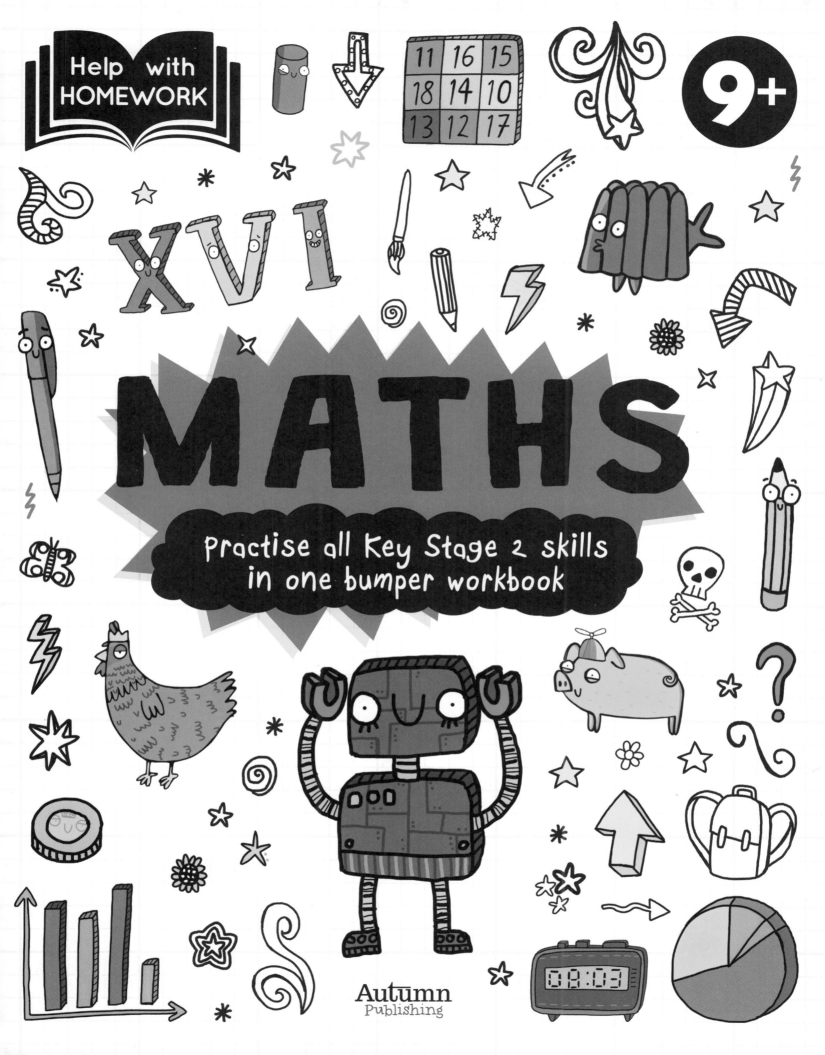

Ordering

When you've finished, give yourself a reward sticker!

Put the cars in order from the smallest number to the largest number using the stickers on the sticker sheet.

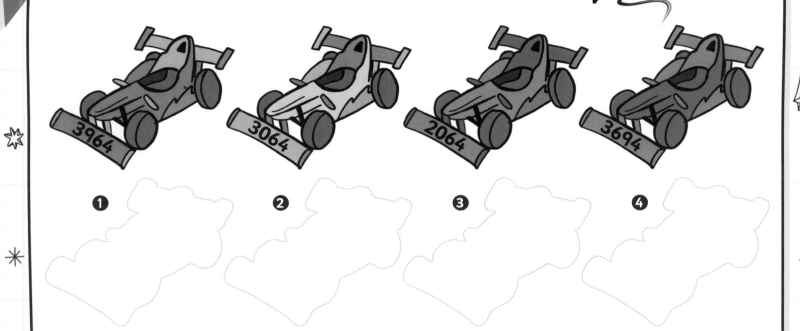

3964   3064   2064   3694

①   ②   ③   ④

Split these numbers into thousands, hundreds, tens and ones.

	Thousands	Hundreds	Tens	Ones
⑤ **3964** =	....	....	....	....
⑥ **1255** =	....	....	....	....
⑦ **993** =	....	....	....	....
⑧ **1050** =	....	....	....	....
⑨ **1004** =	....	....	....	....

Write the numbers from questions 5–9 in order from largest to smallest.

....

STICK A REWARD STICKER HERE

2

Comparing

Look at the pairs of numbers that the characters are holding.
Put a thumbs up sticker next to the largest number in each pair.

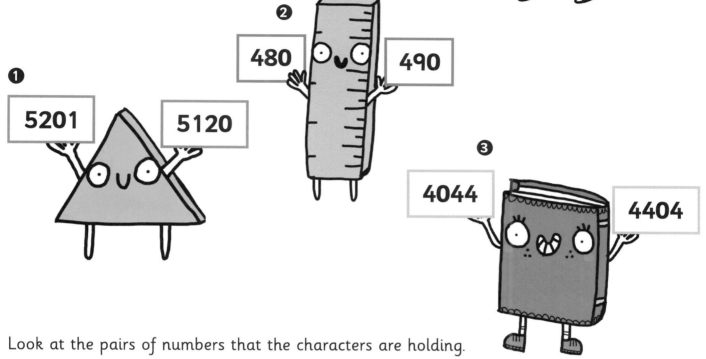

① 5201   5120

② 480   490

③ 4044   4404

Look at the pairs of numbers that the characters are holding.
Put a thumbs up sticker next to the smallest number in each pair.

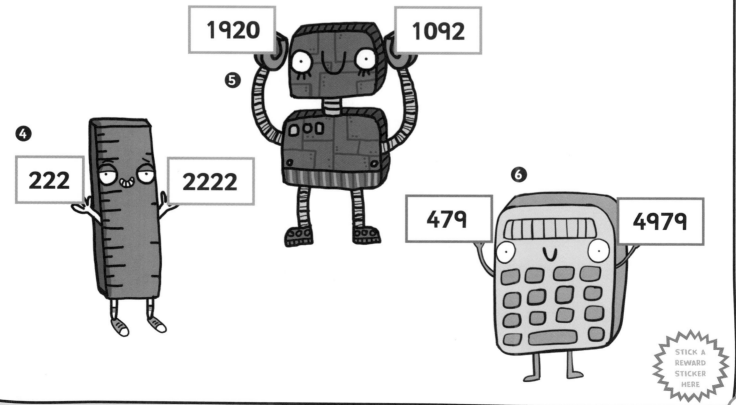

④ 222   2222

⑤ 1920   1092

⑥ 479   4979

STICK A REWARD STICKER HERE

Multiplication

When you've finished, give yourself a reward sticker!

Unicorn finds multiplication complicated! Can you help him by completing the multiplication calculations below in your head?

① **2 x 2 =** ....

② **3 x 4 =** ....

③ **5 x 2 =** ....

④ **8 x 1 =** ....

⑤ **0 x 6 =** ....

⑥ **8 x 7 =** ....

⑦ **9 x 10 =** ....

⑧ **11 x 4 =** ....

⑨ **6 x 12 =** ....

What do unicorns call their dad? Pop Corn!

Complete the multiplication calculations below using a written method to show Unicorn exactly how to work them out.

⑩ **98 x 29** ....

⑪ **66 x 19** ....

⑫ **83 x 85** ....

Camelon

Division

Answer the division calculations below.

① 2 ÷ 2 = ...

② 8 ÷ 4 = ...

③ 20 ÷ 2 = ...

④ 8 ÷ 2 = ...

⑤ 6 ÷ 1 = ...

⑥ 24 ÷ 6 = ...

⑦ 42 ÷ 7 = ...

⑧ 12 ÷ 2 = ...

⑨ 56 ÷ 7 = ...

Complete the division calculations below using a written method.

⑩ 100 ÷ 2 ....

Purr-tle

⑪ 117 ÷ 3 ....

⑫ 228 ÷ 4 ....

⑬ 190 ÷ 10 ....

STICK A
REWARD
STICKER
HERE

Rounding whole numbers

When you've finished, give yourself a reward sticker!

Round these numbers to the nearest 10.

❶ 127 = ...

❷ 382 = ...

❸ 4992 = ...

❹ 1124 = ...

I'm good at <u>rounding up!</u>

Round these numbers to the nearest 100.

❺ 496 = ...

❻ 493 = ...

❼ 399 = ...

❽ 114 = ...

Round these numbers to the nearest 1000.

❾ 4995 = ...

❿ 3811 = ...

⓫ 3002 = ...

⓬ 6039 = ...

Whooooo's clever?

STICK A REWARD STICKER HERE

Roman numerals

Number	1	5	10	50	100	500
Roman numeral	I	V	X	L	C	D

Use the stickers on the sticker sheet to change the numbers below into Roman numerals, then write them out in words. The first one has been done for you.

❶ 10 = X = ...ten.........

❷ 20 = = ...

❸ 50 = = ...

❹ 100 = = ...

❺ 150 = = ...

❻ 200 = = ...

❼ 230 = = ...

❽ 265 = = ...

❾ 380 = = ...

❿ 550 = = ...

STICK A REWARD STICKER HERE

Alien addition

These aliens need help with the addition calculations below. Can you fill in the blanks?

❶ 120 + ☐40 = 260

❷ 175 + 1☐2 = 297

❸ 505 + 1☐1 = 606

❹ 1000 + 1☐5☐ = 2458

Answer the calculations below.

❺ 120 + 40 = ...

❻ 174 + 72 = ...

❼ 805 + 11 = ...

❽ 107 + 105 = ...

Bleep bloop!

❾ 358 + 715 = ...

❿ 573 + 183 = ...

⓫ 685 + 18 + 48 = ...

⓬ 12 + 485 + 404 = ...

STICK A REWARD STICKER HERE

Answers on page 46

Super Subtraction

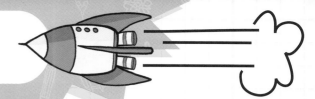

The aliens love eating all sorts of food from Earth. They have filled out the table below which shows how much food they started with and how much they have eaten. Can you work out how much food they have got left?

Food type	Amount started with	Amount eaten	Amount left
Bananas	10	8	....
Pizza	3	3	....
Apples	48	41	....
Ice cream	2	1	....
Cherries	49	36	....
Burgers	24	20	....
Cake	9	8	....

On their way back to the spaceship, the aliens find 59 biscuits. One eats 3, the second one eats 9, another eats 19 and the final alien eats 1. How many biscuits are left? Show your working out.

....

....

....

....

STICK A REWARD STICKER HERE

Prime numbers

When you've finished, give yourself a reward sticker!

A prime number can only be divided by itself or 1. This alien needs to input all prime numbers up to 19 into his spaceship. Can you help him by completing the list below?

❶ __2__ __3__ _____ __7__ _____ __13__ _____ __19__

Work out whether these numbers are prime numbers or not. Show your working and explain how you know. When you've worked it out, put a thumbs up sticker next to every prime number and a thumbs down sticker next to those that are not prime numbers.

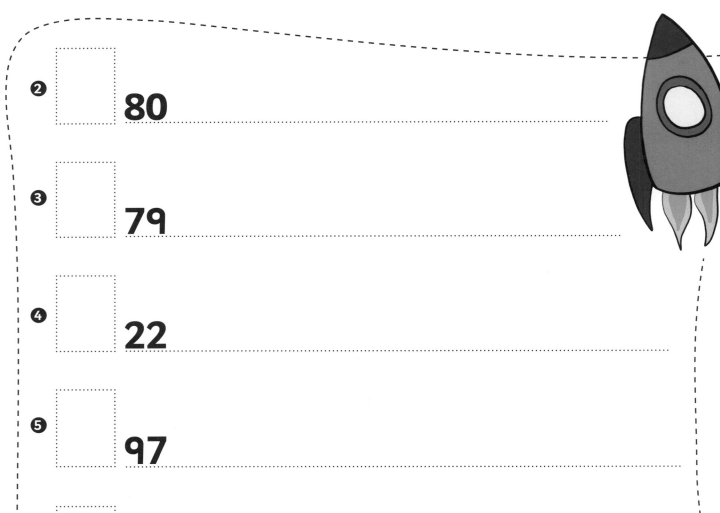

❷ **80**

❸ **79**

❹ **22**

❺ **97**

❻ **98**

STICK A REWARD STICKER HERE

Prime or composite?

A composite number is anything that isn't a prime number. Remember that a prime number can only be divided by itself and one. Look at the numbers below and draw a line to match each one to the correct label. The first one has been done for you.

PRIME NUMBER   **COMPOSITE NUMBER**

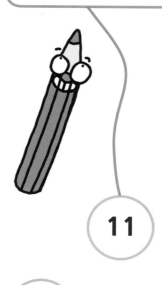

(11)   (70)   (25)   (7)

(40)   (19)   (99)   (72)

Write the numbers below as a product of their prime factors.
The first one is done for you.

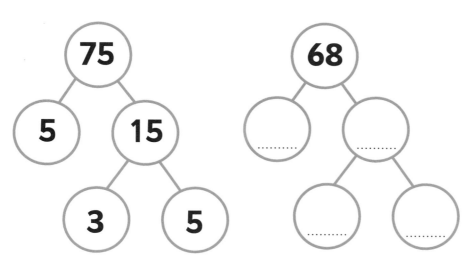

75
5   15
3   5

68
...   ...
...   ...

35
...   ...

Perimeter

Sam wants to put a fence around her fields. Can you work out the perimeter of each field? Write each answer in metres and centimetres.

When you've finished, give yourself a reward sticker!

Remember to add all the sides!

1

9 m

6 m

6 m

9 m

........30........ m
........300........ cm

2

8 m

7 m

........30........ m
........300........ cm

3

4 m

8 m

........24........ m
........240........ cm

4

6 m

5 m

........22........ m
........220........ cm

5

8 m

9 m

........34........ m
........340........ cm

The fence sections Sam will use are 2 m each in length.
How many fence sections does she need in total for all 5 fields?

....

STICK A REWARD STICKER HERE

Area

Help John work out the area of the ponds at a nearby fishing lake.

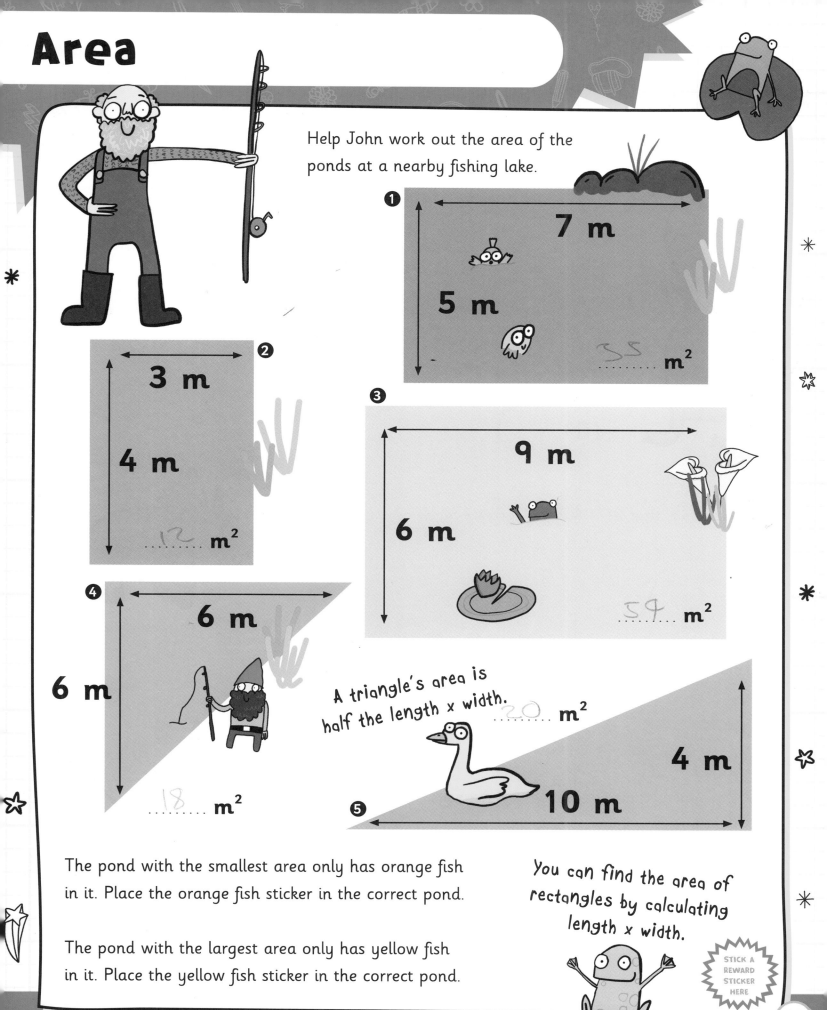

1 7 m
5 m
35 m²

2 3 m
4 m
12 m²

3 9 m
6 m
54 m²

4 6 m
6 m
18 m²

A triangle's area is half the length x width.
20 m²

5 10 m
4 m

The pond with the smallest area only has orange fish in it. Place the orange fish sticker in the correct pond.

The pond with the largest area only has yellow fish in it. Place the yellow fish sticker in the correct pond.

You can find the area of rectangles by calculating length x width.

STICK A REWARD STICKER HERE

Square numbers

When you've finished, give yourself a reward sticker!

Work out the square numbers below. The first one has been done for you.

3^2 = 3 x 3 = 9

5^2 = 5 x 5 =

6^2 =

8^2 =

10^2 =

❶ T-rex says that 2^2 is 4. Is he correct? Show how you know.

....

....

❷ Triceratops has worked out that 11^2 is 22. What has he done wrong? Explain the correct answer.

....

....

❸ Diplodocus thinks 8^2 is 64 but T-rex says that 8^2 is 66. Who is correct? Explain how you know.

....

....

....

STICK A REWARD STICKER HERE

Answers on page 46

Cube numbers

A number is cubed when it is multiplied by itself three times.
Work out the cube numbers below. Show your working.

3^3 =   **3 x 3** x 3 = **9** x 3 = 27

4^3 =   **4 x 4** x 4 = **16** x 4 =

5^3 =

7^3 =

10^3 =

How do you ask a dinosaur to lunch? "Tea, Rex?"

Rawr!

❶ Diplodocus says that 6^3 is 216. Is she correct? Show how you know.

....

....

❷ T-rex says that 9^3 is 27. What has he done wrong? Explain the correct answer.

....

....

❸ Triceratops and T-rex try to work out 12^3. Can you show them the best way to work it out and find the answer?

....

....

....

15

Rounding decimals

When you've finished, give yourself a reward sticker!

Round the decimals below to the nearest whole number.

1 **5.39** ....

2 **5.81** ....

3 **2.05** ....

4 **9.92** ....

purrr-ple

Round the decimals below to one decimal place.

5 **4.54** ....

6 **2.11** ....

7 **9.56** ....

8 **8.32** ....

9 **3.92** ....

10 Now put your answers from questions 5–9 in order from lowest to highest.

....

Percentages

Answer the multiple choice questions below by placing a thumbs up sticker next to each correct answer.

pup-eroni...
my favourite!

❶ $\frac{1}{2}$ as a percentage is   **40%**   **50%**   **60%**

❷ 30% as a decimal is   **0.3**   **0.5**   **0.03**

❸ 0.75 as a percentage is   **55%**   **65%**   **75%**

❹ 20% as a decimal is   **0.22**   **0.2**   **0.02**

❺ If Dog has a whole pizza and she eats half of it, what percentage of the pizza is left?

50%   **90%**   **12%**

❻ Cat bakes a cake and takes 75% of it to his friend's house.
What percentage does he have left at home?

5%   **15%**   **25%**

❼ Cat-ula makes a pie and cuts it into 10 equal slices.
He eats 20% of the slices. What percentage does he have left?

20%   **80%**   **30%**

Vam-purrr

STICK A REWARD STICKER HERE

17

Multiplication

When we multiply a number by 10, each digit moves one place value column to the left. When we multiply a number by 100, each digit moves two place value columns to the left.

For example:

1.5 x 10 = 15
1.5 x 100 = 150

100	10	1	.	0.1
		1	.	5
	1	5	.	0

Jelly-fish

Work out the calculations below.

❶ **4.6 x 10 =** ....

❷ **4.6 x 100 =** ....

❸ **8.8 x 100 =** ....

❹ **9.3 x 100 =** ....

❺ **8.9 x 100 =** ....

❻ **3.75 x 10 =** ....

❼ **4.85 x 100 =** ....

❽ **9.12 x 10 =** ....

❾ **5.55 x 100 =** ....

You're doing turtley awesome!

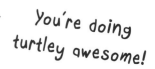

18

Division

When we divide a number by 10, each digit moves one place value column to the right. When we divide by 100, each digit moves two place value columns to the right.

For example:

1.5 ÷ 10 = 0.15

1.5 ÷ 100 = 0.015

I need to wear glasses to improve my di-vision.

Help Octopus work out the calculations below.

❶ 460 ÷ 100 = ...

❷ 460 ÷ 100 = ...

❸ 46 ÷ 10 = ...

❹ 930 ÷ 100 = ...

❺ 850 ÷ 100 = ...

❻ 375 ÷ 10 = ...

❼ 485 ÷ 100 = ...

❽ 910 ÷ 10 = ...

❾ 555 ÷ 100 = ...

STICK A
REWARD
STICKER
HERE

19

2D shapes

When you've finished, give yourself a reward sticker!

Draw the correct 2D shape under each name.

Triangle

Pentagon

Hexagon

Square

Circle

Octagon

True or false? Give each statement a thumbs up sticker if it is true, or turn the sticker round and give it a thumbs down if it is false.

❶ Hexagons have six sides.

❷ Squares have four equal sides.

❸ Octagons have nine sides.

❹ Pentagons have the same number of sides as squares.

❺ Circles have one vertex.

STICK A REWARD STICKER HERE

Answers on page 47

3D Shapes

Place the correct 3D shape sticker under each name, then write a property of each shape underneath.

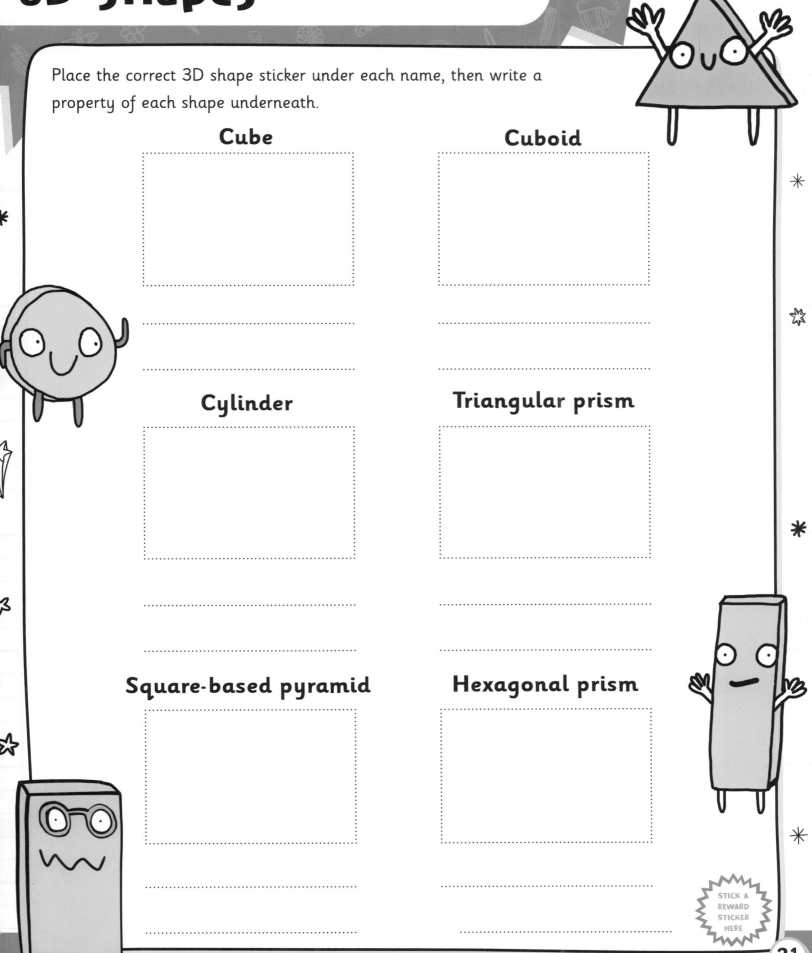

Cube

Cuboid

Cylinder

Triangular prism

Square-based pyramid

Hexagonal prism

STICK A REWARD STICKER HERE

Angles in triangles

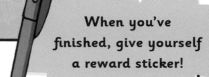

When you've finished, give yourself a reward sticker!

An angle is a measure of turn, or rotation around a point.
We can measure an angle using a protractor.

There are four types of angles:
- Right angle (a quarter turn)
- Acute angle (less than a quarter turn)
- Obtuse angle (between a quarter and a half turn)
- Reflex angle (more than a half turn)

If you add up the angles in a triangle, you always get 180°.

Use calculations to work out the missing angles in these triangles (not to scale).

1 ?° You're acute. 90° 55°

You're all right. **2** ?° 50° 45°

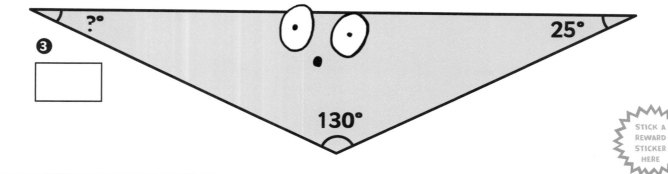

3 ?° 25° 130°

STICK A REWARD STICKER HERE

Missing angles

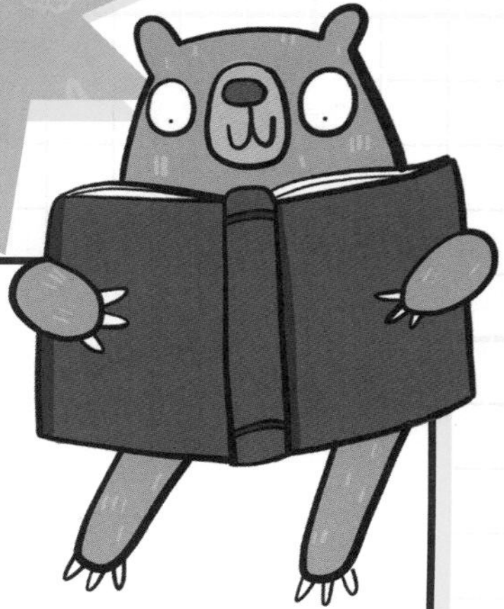

Can you work out the missing angles below? Remember that angles on a straight line add up to 180° and angles around a point add up to 360°.

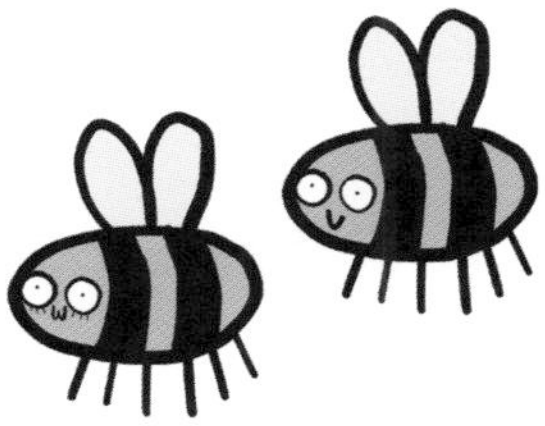

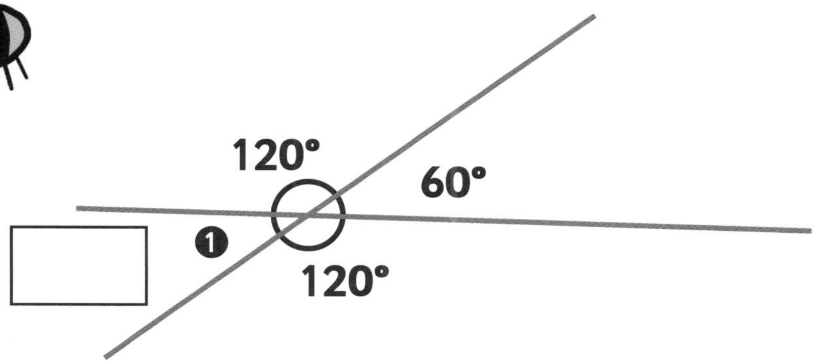

120°
60°
1
120°

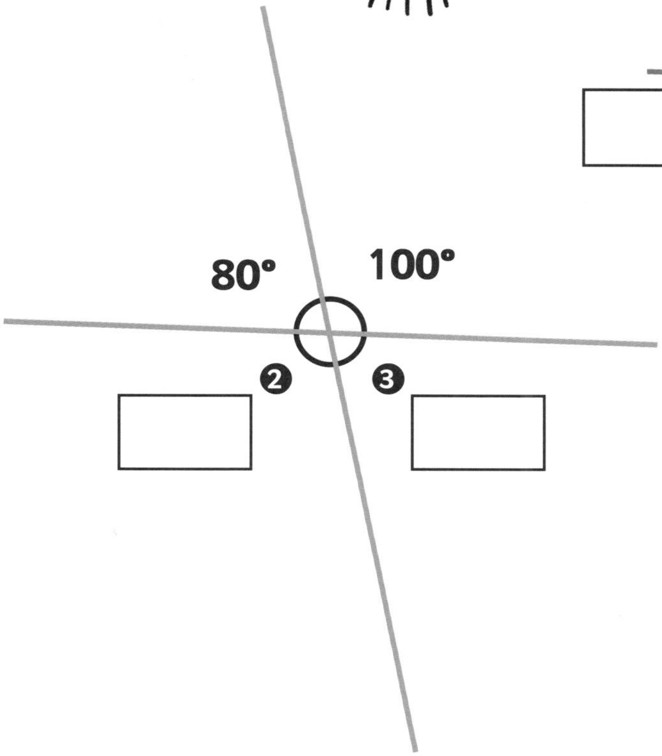

80°
100°
2
3

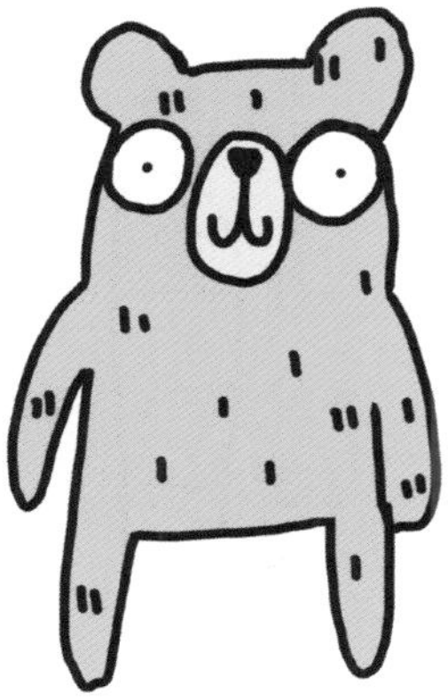

What's a bear without bees? An ear!

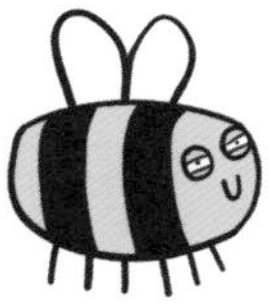

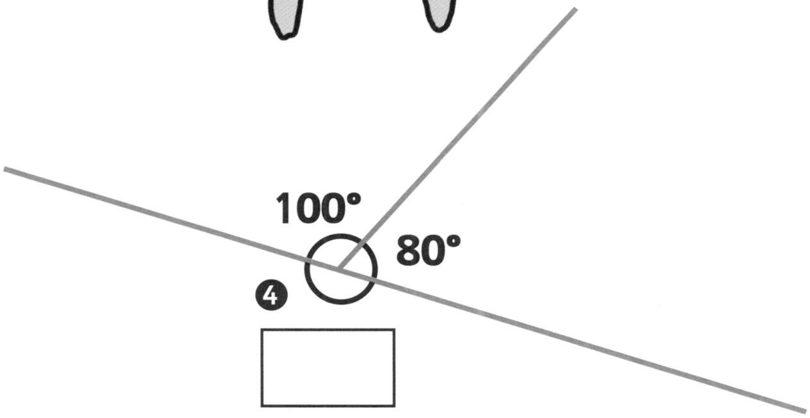

100°
80°
4

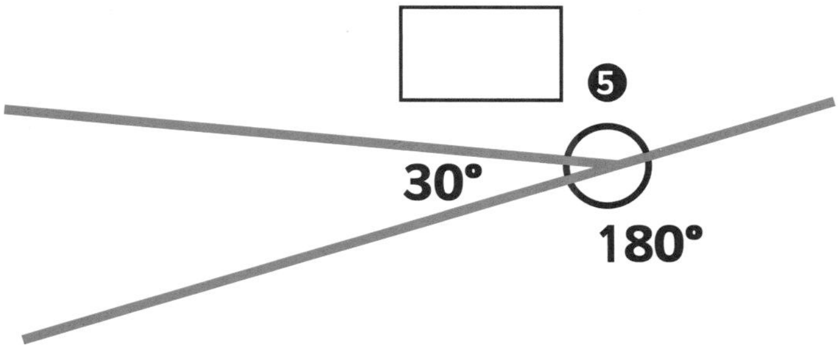

5
30°
180°

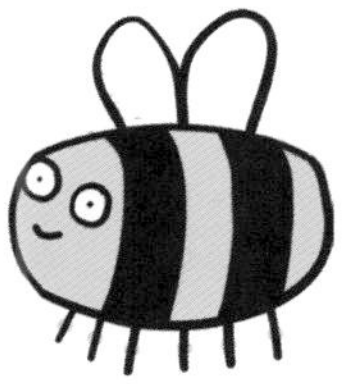

STICK A REWARD STICKER HERE

Answers on page 47

Reading scales

When you've finished, give yourself a reward sticker!

Can you read the thermometers below, and write the temperature on the dotted line for each one?

1

°C
25
20
15
10
5
0
.................°C

2

°C
10
8
6
4
2
0
.................°C

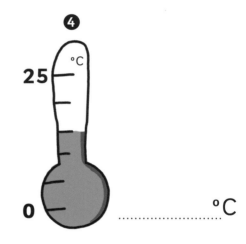

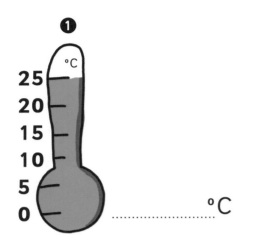

N-ice!

3

°C
50
40
30
20
10
0
.................°C

4

°C
25
0
.................°C

5

°C
25
0
.................°C

6

°C
60
10
.................°C

STICK A REWARD STICKER HERE

24

Pirate coordinates

Captain Sloth has forgotten where his treasure chests are buried! Find the coordinates in the grid below and place a treasure chest sticker on each point. One has been done for you.

(–5,6) (4,4) (–2,–3) (2,2) (–3,–3) (1,1)

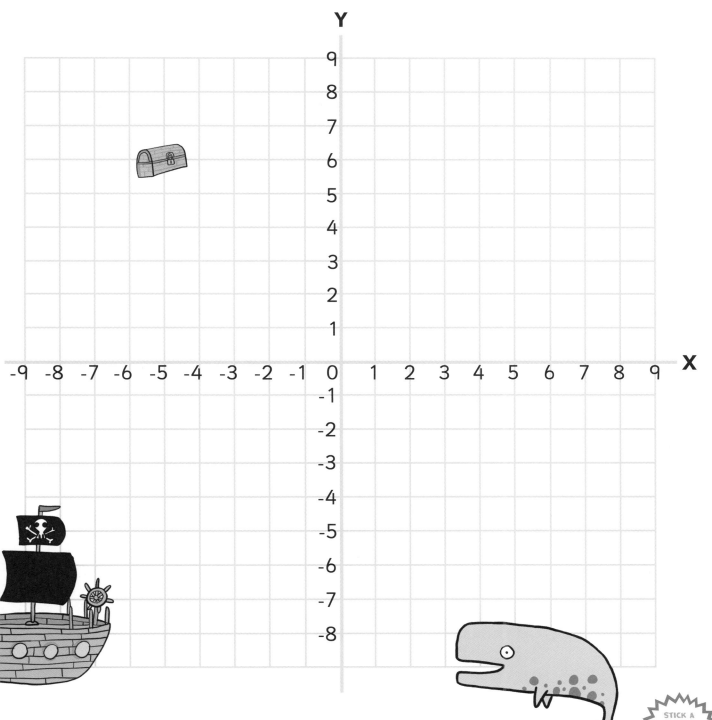

Polygons

The shapes below are regular or irregular polygons. Label each one using a sticker from the sticker sheet. Write the name of the regular polygons underneath. The first one has been done for you.

When you've finished, give yourself a reward sticker!

①

....
regular
....
square
....

②

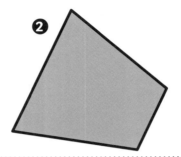

....

....

③

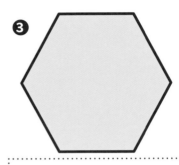

....

....

④

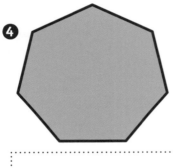

....

....

⑤

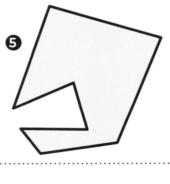

....

....

⑥

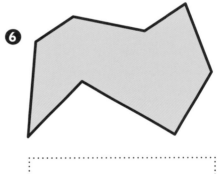

....

....

⑦

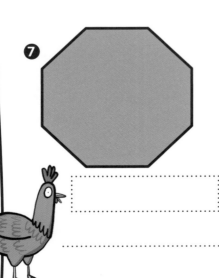

....

....

⑧

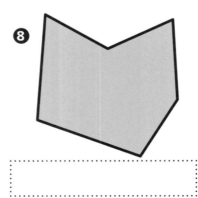

....

....

⑨

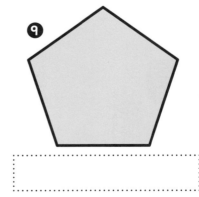

....

....

STICK A REWARD STICKER HERE

26

Regular or irregular?

Draw two regular polygons. How do you know they are regular?
Write a reason on the dotted lines.

....

....

Draw two irregular polygons. How do you know they are irregular?
Write a reason on the dotted lines.

....

....

Reflections

When you've finished, give yourself a reward sticker!

Reflection is a type of transformation where a shape is reflected in a mirror line.

Look at the reflections below. Three are correct and three are incorrect. Place a thumbs up sticker next to the correct reflections.

This is the mirror line

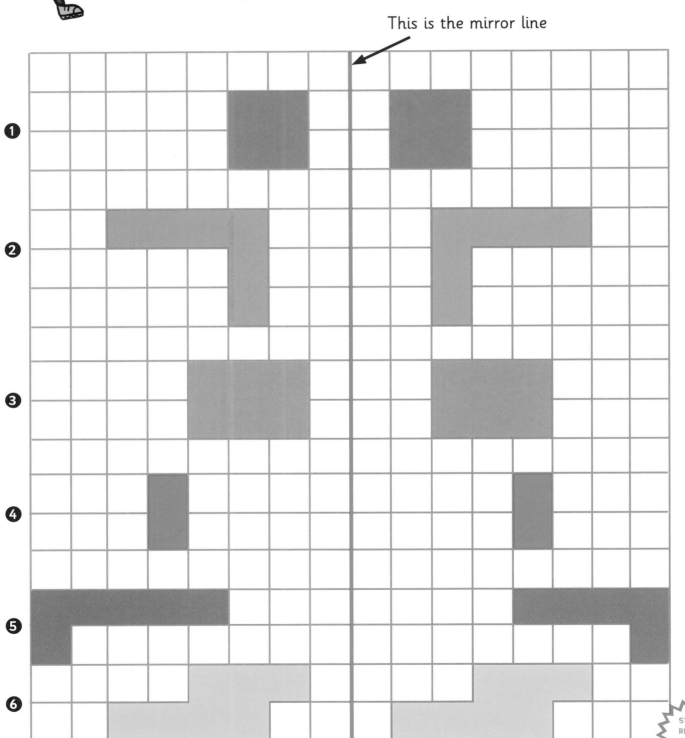

1

2

3

4

5

6

STICK A REWARD STICKER HERE

Answers on page 47

More reflections

Use the hexagon sticker on the sticker sheet to show the reflection of this shape.

Draw your own shape on the left-hand side then draw its reflection to the right of the mirror line.

STICK A
REWARD
STICKER
HERE

Answers on page 47

Translation

Translation is when a shape is moved from its original position to a new position, without turning or rotating.

 For example, the shape below has moved 4 squares to the right.

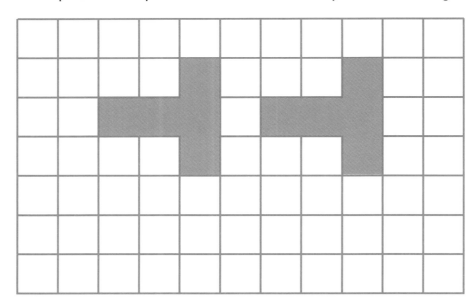

In the grid below, using the stickers on your sticker sheet, move the purple shape 5 squares down, then move the pink shape 2 squares to the left and 4 squares up.

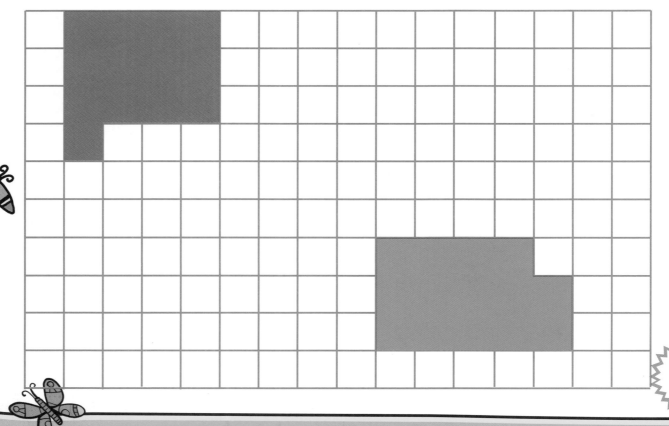

STICK A REWARD STICKER HERE

Sequences

Fill in the blanks in the number sequences below. Write the rule underneath each one. The first rule has been done for you.

10 20 ☐ 40 50 60 70 ☐ 90 100 ☐ 120

...... Add 10 each time ....

5 10 15 20 ☐ 30 35 ☐ 45 ☐ ☐ 60

....

3 6 9 12 15 ☐ 21 ☐ 27 ☐ 33 ☐

....

1 2 4 7 11 ☐ 22 29 37 46 ☐ ☐

....

Write out two of your own number sequences and write the rule underneath each one.

☐ ☐ ☐ ☐ ☐ ☐ ☐ ☐

....

☐ ☐ ☐ ☐ ☐ ☐ ☐ ☐

....

School timetable

When you've finished, give yourself a reward sticker!

The timetable below shows the times of Year 5 lessons for the week. Answer the questions about the timetable below.

	Lesson 1	Lesson 2	B R E A K T I M E	Lesson 3	Lesson 4	L U N C H T I M E	Lesson 5	Lesson 6
Monday	Maths	English		History	Assembly		Geography	Music
Tuesday	English	Maths		Drama	Assembly		History	P.E.
Wednesday	Maths	English		French	Assembly		Music	Art
Thursday	English	Maths		Maths	P.E.		French	R.E.
Friday	English	English		Maths	Assembly		Art	Art

❶ Which days have a History lesson? ....

❷ How many Maths classes are there per week? ....

❸ What are the two most common classes? ....

❹ Is Geography after break time or lunch time? ....

❺ What is straight after English on a Tuesday? ....

❻ How many lessons are there on Wednesdays? ....

❼ Which day has two art lessons? ....

❽ Which day doesn't have assembly? ....

STICK A REWARD STICKER HERE

Your own table

Make your own timetable for your weekend. Include at least 5 events each day.
For example, events could include reading a book, playing a board game or baking.

	7am–9am	9am–11am	11am–1pm	1pm–3pm	3pm–5pm	5pm–7pm	7pm–9pm
Saturday							
Sunday							

Which event do you do most on a Saturday? ....

How many events have you included in total? ....

Are there any time slots when you don't have an event? ....

Draw your own table in the box below to show what you eat throughout a typical day.
You could use the following headings: Breakfast / Snack / Lunch / Tea / Dinner / Dessert.

Simplifying fractions

When you've finished, give yourself a reward sticker!

Simplify the fractions below to their simplest form.

1 $\dfrac{4}{10}$ ....

2 $\dfrac{2}{40}$ ....

3 $\dfrac{10}{100}$ ....

4 $\dfrac{30}{90}$ ....

Add the following fractions then simplify the answer to its simplest form.

5 $\dfrac{4}{20} + \dfrac{8}{20} =$ ....

6 $\dfrac{3}{10} + \dfrac{2}{10} =$ ....

STICK A REWARD STICKER HERE

Answers on page 48

Ordering fractions

Simplify the fractions below so that they all have 10 as their denominator.

1 $\dfrac{80}{100}$ ....

2 $\dfrac{20}{100}$ ....

3 $\dfrac{60}{100}$ ....

What does a lion do on a canoe? Use his roar!

4 $\dfrac{10}{100}$ ....

5 $\dfrac{50}{100}$ ....

Now write the simplified fractions from smallest to largest in the boxes below.

Adding fractions

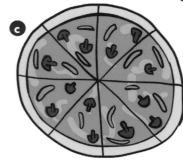

When you've finished, give yourself a reward sticker!

Llama and his friends have ordered three pizzas for their weekend treat. Each pizza has 8 slices.

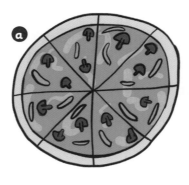

a

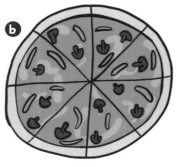

b

c

"Waiter, will my pizza be long?"
"No, sir. It will be round!"

They eat $\frac{1}{2}$ of Pizza A, $\frac{3}{4}$ of Pizza B and $\frac{1}{8}$ of Pizza C. Place the correct number of pizza slice stickers in the box to show how many slices they have got left over.

Fill in the missing denominators and numerators using the stickers on the sticker sheet.

❶ $\frac{2}{5} + \frac{1}{5} = \frac{\Box}{5}$

❷ $\frac{11}{13} + \frac{1}{13} = \frac{\Box}{\Box}$

❸ $\frac{2}{10} + \frac{\Box}{10} = \frac{8}{10}$

❹ $\frac{21}{37} + \frac{\Box}{37} = \frac{29}{\Box}$

❺ $\frac{9}{20} + \frac{3}{\Box} = \frac{\Box}{20}$

❻ $\frac{19}{23} + \frac{2}{\Box} = \frac{\Box}{23}$

STICK A REWARD STICKER HERE

Answers on page 48

Subtracting fractions

The following weekend, Llama and his friends take a homemade cake to a charity bake sale. The cake is split into 12 slices, and they sell 8 slices. What fraction of the cake is left? Show your working.

....

....

....

The following day, Llama takes two cakes into another school bake sale. One is split into 20 slices and they sell 16. The other is split into 10 slices and they sell 8. What fraction of each cake is left?

....

....

Fill in the missing denominators and numerators using the stickers on the sticker sheet.

① $\dfrac{4}{5} - \dfrac{1}{5} = \dfrac{\boxed{}}{5}$

② $\dfrac{12}{13} - \dfrac{5}{13} = \dfrac{\boxed{}}{\boxed{}}$

③ $\dfrac{4}{10} - \dfrac{\boxed{}}{10} = \dfrac{3}{10}$

④ $\dfrac{17}{18} - \dfrac{10}{18} = \dfrac{\boxed{}}{\boxed{}}$

⑤ $\dfrac{9}{25} - \dfrac{3}{\boxed{}} = \dfrac{\boxed{}}{25}$

⑥ $\dfrac{19}{23} - \dfrac{2}{\boxed{}} = \dfrac{\boxed{}}{23}$

Is it mm, cm or m?

When you've finished, give yourself a reward sticker!

Convert the measurements between metres (m) and centimetres (cm).

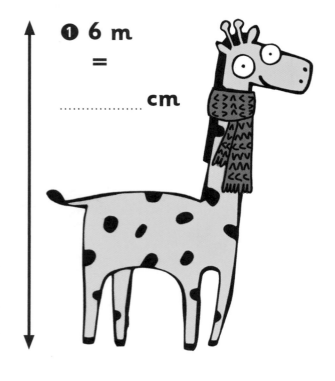

❶ 6 m
=

.... cm

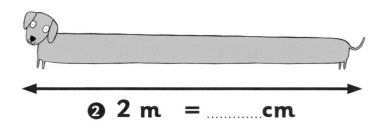

❷ 2 m = ...cm

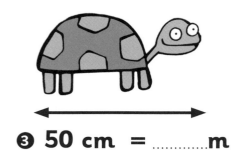

❸ 50 cm = ...m

Wanda Worm and her friends are trying to work out who is the longest. Can you convert the centimetre (cm) measurements to millimetres (mm)?

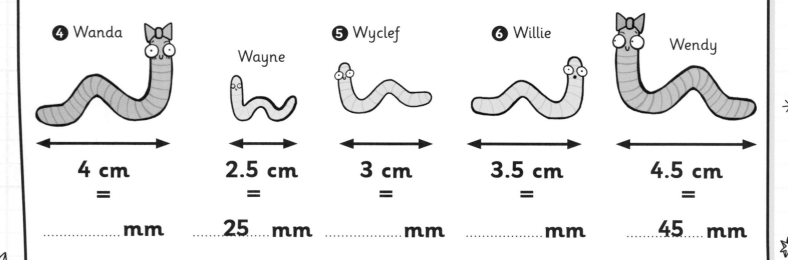

❹ Wanda

Wayne

❺ Wyclef

❻ Willie

Wendy

4 cm	2.5 cm	3 cm	3.5 cm	4.5 cm
=	=	=	=	=
.... mm	....25.... mm	.... mm	.... mm	...45.... mm

Who is the longest worm? ....

How many millimetres is the shortest worm? ....

STICK A REWARD STICKER HERE

Jam, grams and kilograms

Convert the jam weight from kilograms (kg) to grams (g).

1 Each jar holds 2 kg of jam. Clown has made 6000 g of jam. How many jars can he fill? Show your working.

We're jammin'!

....

....

3 **2 kg** = ... **g**

2 If Clown has three jars half-filled with jam and two full jars of jam, how much do they weigh in kilograms?

4 **1 kg** = ... **g**

....

5 Clown sells his jars of jam to his friends. One of his friends wants 5 kg of jam. How many jars should Clown give him? Show your working.

....

....

6 Clown gives his family 6000 g of jam. How much is that in kilograms? Show your working.

....

....

Buuuuuuuuuuuuuurrrrp!

7 In one month, Clown eats 2 kg of jam. The next month, he eats 3 kg of jam. How much has he eaten in grams?

....

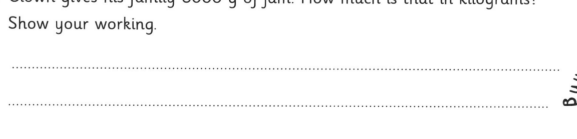

8 Clown makes a new batch of jam and fills up 120 jars. How many kilograms is that?

....

STICK A REWARD STICKER HERE

Radius

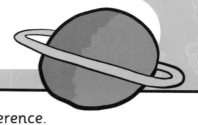

When you've finished, give yourself a reward sticker!

A circle has a radius, diameter and circumference.
The radius and diameter can be measured with a ruler.

The radius is the distance half way across a circle.
Can you tick the image below that correctly shows the radius?

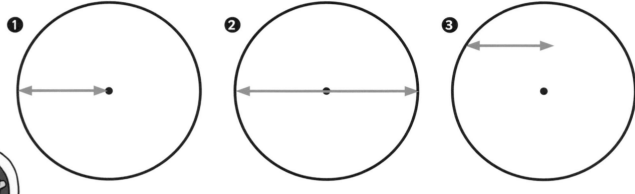

① ② ③

Amy the Astronaut has just arrived back at Earth after a mission in space. She found three new planets! Can you help her measure the radius of each of the planets? Remember to use a ruler.

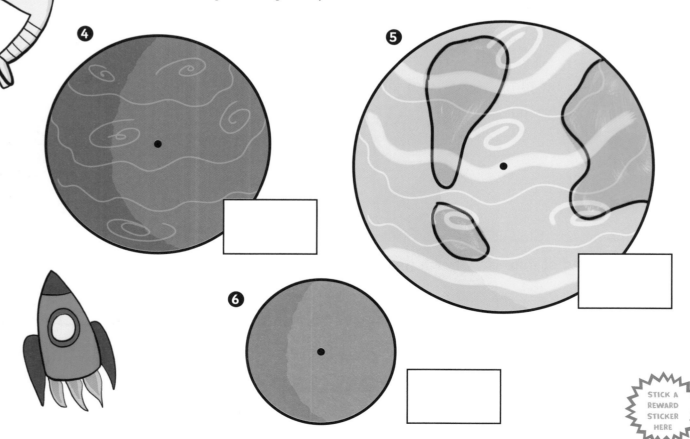

④

⑤

⑥

STICK A
REWARD
STICKER
HERE

Answers on page 48

Diameter

The diameter is the distance across the middle of a circle.

Can you tick the image below that correctly shows the diameter?

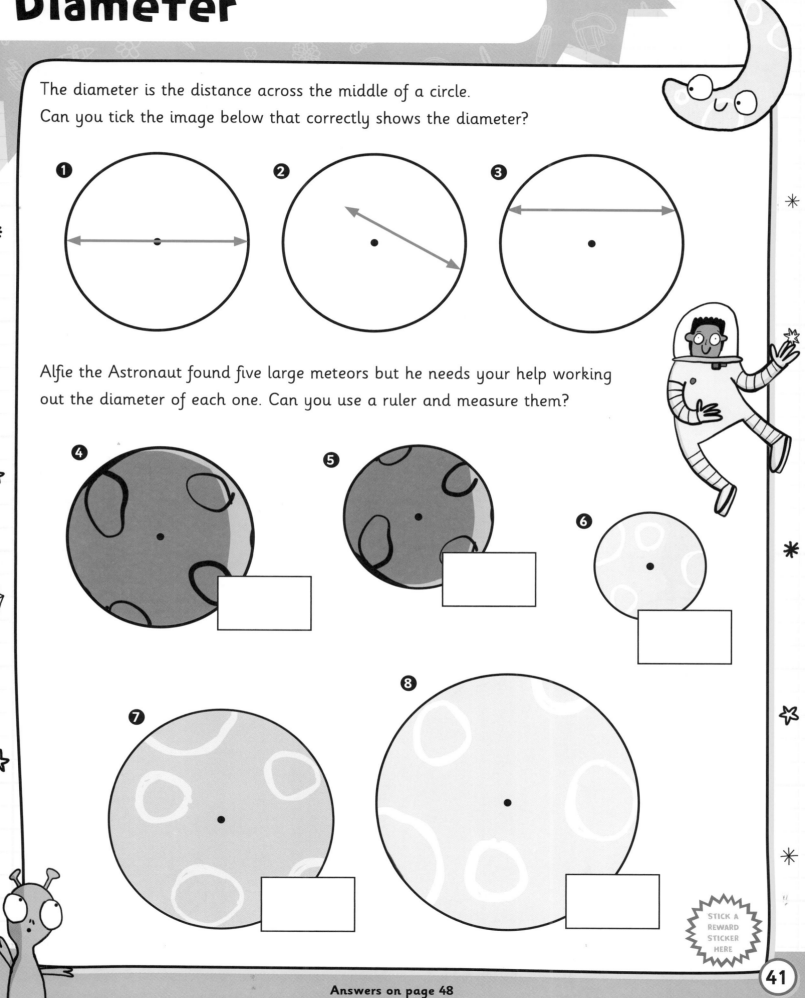

Alfie the Astronaut found five large meteors but he needs your help working out the diameter of each one. Can you use a ruler and measure them?

STICK A
REWARD
STICKER
HERE

41

Circumference

When you've finished, give yourself a reward sticker!

The circumference is the distance all the way around a circle.

Can you tick the image below that correctly shows the circumference?

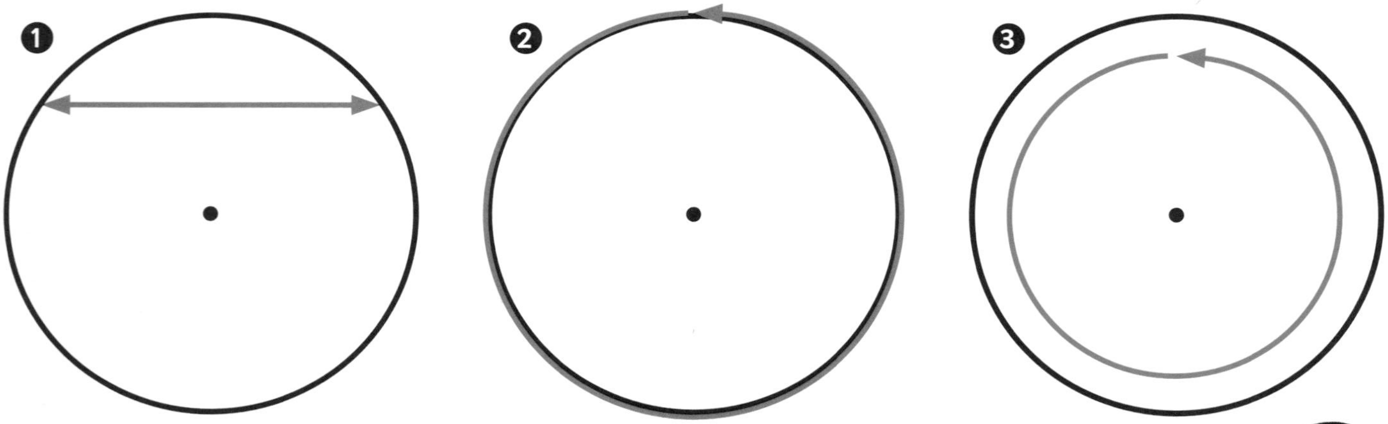

1

2

3

Amy also found some Moons on her space mission. Can you use the stickers on the sticker sheet to put them in order from smallest circumference to largest circumference? *The stickers are not to scale.*

Moon A
24.5 km
circumference

Moon B
57.1 km
circumference

Moon C
21.09 km
circumference

Moon D
21.9 km
circumference

Moon E
57.7 km
circumference

STICK A REWARD STICKER HERE

Answers on page 48

Percentages

There is a sale at the local shop and the cashier needs your help to work out the new prices.

1 A customer brings a pair of shoes to the till to pay. They are £32 and have 50% off. How much should the cashier charge the customer? Show your working.

....

....

....

2 A customer brings a computer game to the till to pay. It is £150 and has 25% off. How much should the cashier charge the customer? Show your working.

....

....

....

3 A customer brings two pairs of trousers to the till to pay. One pair is £40 and has 10% off. The other pair is £120 and has 60% off. How much should the cashier charge the customer? Show your working.

....

....

....

4 A customer brings a television and a bicycle to the till to pay. The television is £900 and has 50% off. The bicycle is £500 and has 15% off. Which item is the cheapest after discount? Circle it below.

Bar charts

When you've finished, give yourself a reward sticker!

A large group of people were asked what their favourite theme park ride is. This bar chart shows the results.

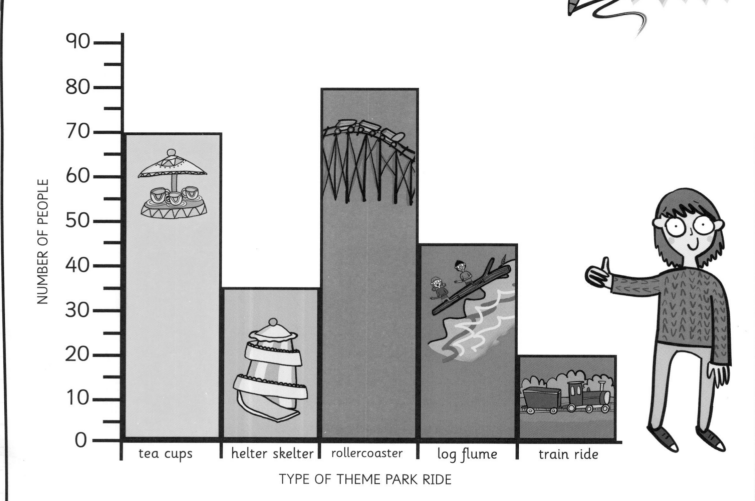

❶ What is the most popular ride? ....

❷ What is the least popular ride? ....

❸ How many people chose the train ride as their favourite? ....

❹ How many people chose the helter skelter as their favourite? ....

❺ Which ride did 45 people choose as their favourite? ....

❻ How many rides are there altogether? ....

STICK A REWARD STICKER HERE

Line graphs

This line graph shows the temperature outside Penguin's home.

What do you call a happy penguin? A Pen-grin!

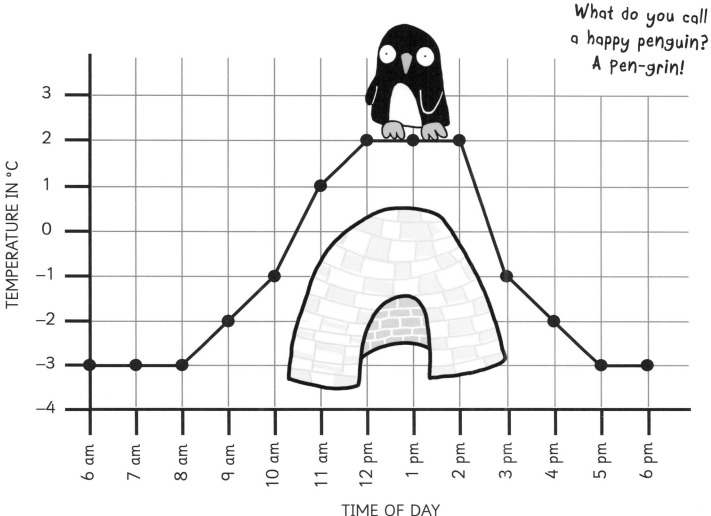

TEMPERATURE IN °C

TIME OF DAY

❶ What temperature was it when Penguin woke up at 7 am? ....

❷ How many degrees did the temperature increase by between 9 am and 11 am? ....

❸ What was the most common temperature between 6 am and 6 pm? ....

❹ How many degrees colder was it at 3 pm than 2 pm? ....

❺ The temperature at 7 pm was 2 degrees colder than at 4 pm.
What was the temperature at 7 pm? ....

STICK A REWARD STICKER HERE

Answers

Page 2: Ordering

Correct order: 2064, 3064, 3694, 3964.

	Thousands	Hundreds	Tens	Ones
5. 3964 =	3000	900	60	4
6. 1255 =	1000	200	50	5
7. 993 =	0	900	90	3
8. 1050 =	1000	0	50	0
9. 1004 =	1000	0	0	4

Correct order: 993, 1004, 1050, 1255, 3964

Page 3: Comparing

1. 5201 **2.** 490 **3.** 4404 **4.** 222 **5.** 1092 **6.** 479

Page 4: Multiplication

1. 4 **2.** 12 **3.** 10 **4.** 8 **5.** 0 **6.** 56 **7.** 90 **8.** 44 **9.** 72 **10.** 2842 **11.** 1254 **12.** 7055

Page 5: Division

1. 1 **2.** 2 **3.** 10 **4.** 4 **5.** 6 **6.** 4 **7.** 6 **8.** 6 **9.** 8 **10.** 50 **11.** 39 **12.** 57 **13.** 19

Bat-suma!

Page 6: Rounding whole numbers

1. 130 **2.** 380 **3.** 4990 **4.** 1120 **5.** 500 **6.** 500 **7.** 400 **8.** 100 **9.** 5000 **10.** 4000 **11.** 3000 **12.** 6000

Page 7: Roman numerals

2. 20=XX=twenty **3.** 50=L=fifty **4.** 100=C=one hundred **5.** 150=CL=one hundred and fifty **6.** 200=CC=two hundred **7.** 230=CCXXX=two hundred and thirty **8.** 265=CCLXV=two hundred and sixty-five **9.** 380=CCCLXXX= three hundred and eighty **10.** 550=DL=five hundred and fifty

Page 8: Alien addition

1. 120 + 140 = 260 **2.** 175 + 122 = 297 **3.** 505 + 101 = 606 **4.** 1000 + 1458 = 2458 **5.** 160 **6.** 246 **7.** 816 **8.** 212 **9.** 1073 **10.** 756 **11.** 751 **12.** 901

Page 9: Super subtraction

Bananas=2, pizza=0, apples=7, ice cream=1, cherries=13, burgers=4, cake=1. 59 − 3 − 9 − 19 − 1 = 27. 27 biscuits are left.

Page 10: Prime numbers

1. 2, 3, 5, 7, 11, 13, 17, 19. **2.** 80: divisible by 2 and 5 so isn't a prime number. **3.** 79: only divisible by 1 and itself so is a prime number. **4.** 22: divisible by 2 so isn't a prime number. **5.** 97: only divisible by 1 and itself so is a prime number. **6.** 98: divisible by 2 so isn't a prime number.

Page 11: Prime or composite?

Prime numbers: 11, 7, 19   Composite numbers: 70, 25, 72, 40, 99

Page 12: Perimeter

1. 30 m / 3000 cm **2.** 30 m / 3000 cm **3.** 24 m / 2400 cm **4.** 22 m / 2200 cm
5. 34 m / 3400 cm. Sam will need 70 fence sections for all 5 fields.

Page 13: Area

1. 35 m² **2.** 12 m² **3.** 54 m² **4.** 18 m² **5.** 20 m². Orange fish = pond 2. Yellow fish = pond 3.

Page 14: Squared numbers

5² 5 x 5 = 25   6² 6 x 6 = 36   8² 8 x 8 = 64   10² 10 x 10 = 100   **1.** T-rex is correct because 2 x 2 = 4.
2. Triceratops has calculated 11 + 11 but should have calculated 11 x 11 = 121.   **3.** Diplodocus is correct because 8 x 8 = 64.

Page 15: Cubed numbers

4³ = 64 5³ = 125 7³ = 343 10³ = 1000 **1.** Diplodocus is correct. **2.** He's done 9 x 3 rather than 9 x 9 x 9 = 729. **3.** 12 x 12 x 12 = 1728

Page 16: Rounding decimals

1. 5.39 = 5 **2.** 5.81 = 6 **3.** 2.05 = 2 **4.** 9.92 = 10 **5.** 4.54 = 4.5 **6.** 2.11 = 2.1 **7.** 9.56 = 9.6 **8.** 8.32 = 8.3 **9.** 3.92 = 3.9 **10.** 2.1, 3.9, 4.5, 8.3, 9.6

Answers

Page 17: Percentages
1. 50% **2.** 0.3 **3.** 75% **4.** 0.2 **5.** 50% **6.** 25% **7.** 80%

Page 18: Multiplication
1. 46 **2.** 460 **3.** 880 **4.** 930 **5.** 890 **6.** 37.5 **7.** 485 **8.** 91.2 **9.** 555

Page 19: Division
1. 4.6 **2.** 4.6 **3.** 4.6 **4.** 9.3 **5.** 8.5 **6.** 37.5 **7.** 4.85 **8.** 91 **9.** 5.55

Page 20: 2D shapes

Triangle Pentagon Hexagon Square Circle Octagon

True: 1, 2 **False:** 3, 4, 5

Page 21: 3D shapes

Cube Cuboid Cylinder Triangular prism Square-based pyramid Hexagonal prism

Page 22: Angles in triangles
1. 35° **2.** 85° **3.** 25°

Page 23: Missing angles
1. 60° **2.** 100° **3.** 80° **4.** 180° **5.** 150°

Page 24: Reading scales
1. 25 °C **2.** 2 °C **3.** 0 °C **4.** 15 °C **5.** 10 °C **6.** 40 °C

Page 26: Polygons
1. regular, square **2.** irregular **3.** regular, hexagon **4.** regular, heptagon
5. irregular **6.** irregular **7.** regular, octagon **8.** irregular **9.** regular, pentagon

Page 28: Reflections
1. Correct **2.** Correct **3.** Incorrect **4.** Correct **5.** Incorrect **6.** Incorrect

Page 29: More reflections

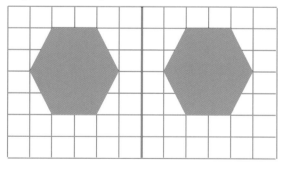

Page 30: Translation

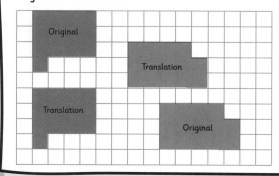

Page 25: Pirate coordinates

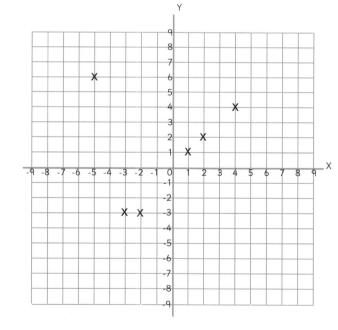

What do you get when you cross a pig and a cactus? A porky-pine!

Answers

Page 31: Sequences
10 20 **30** 40 50 60 70 **80** 90 100 **110** 120 (add 10 each time) / 5 10 15 20 **25** 30 35 **40** 45 **50 55** 60 (add 5 each time) / 3 6 9 12 15 **18** 21 **24** 27 **30** 33 **36** (add 3 each time) / 1 2 4 7 11 **16** 22 29 37 46 **56 67** (add 1, then add 2, then add 3, and so on, increasing by 1 each time)

Page 32: School timetable
1. Monday and Tuesday   **2.** 6   **3.** Maths and English   **4.** Lunch time   **5.** Maths   **6.** 5   **7.** Friday   **8.** Thursday

Page 34: Simplifying fractions
1. $\frac{2}{5}$ **2.** $\frac{1}{20}$ **3.** $\frac{1}{10}$ **4.** $\frac{1}{3}$ **5.** $\frac{3}{5}$ **6.** $\frac{1}{2}$

Page 35: Ordering fractions
1. $\frac{8}{10}$ **2.** $\frac{2}{10}$ **3.** $\frac{6}{10}$ **4.** $\frac{1}{10}$ **5.** $\frac{5}{10}$ In order: $\frac{1}{10}$ $\frac{2}{10}$ $\frac{5}{10}$ $\frac{6}{10}$ $\frac{8}{10}$

Page 36: Adding fractions
Pizza A has 4 slices left. **Pizza B** has 2 slices left. **Pizza C** has 7 slices left. Therefore, there should be 13 pizza slice stickers on the plate.
1. $\frac{2}{5} + \frac{1}{5} = \frac{3}{5}$ **2.** $\frac{11}{13} + \frac{1}{13} = \frac{12}{13}$ **3.** $\frac{2}{10} + \frac{6}{10} = \frac{8}{10}$ **4.** $\frac{21}{37} + \frac{8}{37} = \frac{29}{37}$ **5.** $\frac{9}{20} + \frac{3}{20} = \frac{12}{20}$ **6.** $\frac{19}{23} + \frac{2}{23} = \frac{21}{23}$

Page 37: Subtracting fractions
12 − 8 = 4 slices left which is $\frac{4}{12} = \frac{1}{3}$. 20 − 16 = 4 which is $\frac{4}{20}$. 10 − 8 = 2 which is $\frac{2}{10}$. These two fractions simplified are: $\frac{1}{5}$ and $\frac{1}{5}$
1. $\frac{4}{5} - \frac{1}{5} = \frac{3}{5}$ **2.** $\frac{12}{13} - \frac{5}{13} = \frac{7}{13}$ **3.** $\frac{4}{10} - \frac{1}{10} = \frac{3}{10}$ **4.** $\frac{17}{18} - \frac{10}{18} = \frac{7}{18}$ **5.** $\frac{9}{25} - \frac{3}{25} = \frac{6}{25}$ **6.** $\frac{19}{23} - \frac{2}{23} = \frac{17}{23}$

Page 38: Is it mm, cm or m?
1. 600 cm   **2.** 200 cm   **3.** 0.5 m   **4.** 40 mm   **5.** 25 mm   **6.** 30 mm   **7.** 35 mm   **8.** 45 mm
Wendy is the longest worm. The shortest worm is 25 mm (Wayne).

Page 39: Jam, grams and kilograms
1. 3 jars   **2.** 3 jars half-filled = 3 kg. 2 full jars = 4 kg. So 3 kg + 4 kg = 7 kg in total.   **3.** 2000 g   **4.** 1000 g
5. Two full jars and one half-full jar.   **6.** 6 kg   **7.** 5000 g   **8.** 120 x 2 kg = 240 kg

Page 40: Radius
Circle 1 is correct.   **4.** 3 cm (30 mm)   **5.** 4 cm (40 mm)   **6.** 2 cm (20 mm)

Page 41: Diameter
Circle 1 is correct.   **4.** 5 cm (50 mm)   **5.** 4 cm (40 mm)   **6.** 3 cm (30 mm)   **7.** 6 cm (60 mm)   **8.** 7 cm (70 mm)

Page 42: Circumference
Circle 2 is correct. Correct order is: Moon C, Moon D, Moon A, Moon B, Moon E.

Page 43: Percentages
1. 32 − 16 = £16   **2.** 150 − 37.5 = £112.50   **3.** 40 − 4 = 36 and 120 − 72 = 48 so 36 + 48 = £84
4. 900 − 450 = £450 (television). 500 − 75 = £425 (bicycle).
Therefore, the bicycle is the cheapest after discount.

Page 44: Bar charts
1. rollercoaster   **2.** train ride   **3.** 20   **4.** 35   **5.** log flume   **6.** 5

Page 45: Line graphs
1. −3°C   **2.** 3   **3.** −3 °C   **4.** 3   **5.** −4 °C

Well done!